Now I Am Five

Contents

Now I Am Five

I know heaps,
Now I'm five and not four,
And when I'm six
I bet I'll know more.

I Can Jump

I can jump,
I can hop,
I can run,
I can flop,
I can sit,
I can lie,
But
I
can't
fly.

I Am Me!

I am not
a crocodile,
I am not
a bee,
I am not
a monkey.
I am
me!

The Roller-coaster

In the roller-coaster —
whizzing, whizzing, whee!
Up
and
down,
In and out,
I scream,
I yell,
I screech,
I shout —
A dizzy, dizzy me.

I'm Glad I'm Not . . .

I am glad I'm not a hippo,
I am glad I'm not a frog,
I am glad I'm not an elephant,
I am glad I'm not a dog.

But . . .

I wish I was a monkey
With a funny face
And a long, long tail,
To swing from place to place.

I am glad I'm not a kangaroo,
I am glad I'm not a bat,
I am glad I'm not a bumblebee,
I am glad I'm not a cat.

But . . .

I wish I was a monkey,
Living in a tree,
Then I could make a monkey face —
I can't when I am me.

Here Is an Egg

Here is an egg.
It is going to break.
What will come out?
A bird or a snake?

I Can

"I can't,"
said the sleepyhead.
"Not I."

"I can't,"
said the slowpoke.
"Not I."

"I can't,"
said the lazybones.
"Not I."

But me?
I can, if I try.

I Love to . . .

I love to go to the beach,
I love to play in the sun,
I love to splash in the water,
I love having fun.

I Might Be . . .

I am not
a grandpa,

I am not
a grandma,

I am not
a father,

I am not
a mother,

BUT . . .

I might be
a sister or a brother.

I Like Jam

I like jam,
But
I don't like ham.

I like pies,
But
I don't like flies.

I like green
And red and blue.
I like me
And I like you!

I like cats,
But
I don't like rats.

I like bees,
But
I don't like fleas.

I like pink
And orange, too.
I like me
And I like you!

I Wrote a Story

I wrote a story.
I made a book.
I wrote a story.
Come and look!

Looking at the Clouds

Sometimes I lie
in the grass,
And I look at the clouds
up high,
And I dream I am riding
a white horse,
And I'm galloping over the sky.

Little Bird

"Little bird,
  Little bird,
Why can't you fly?"

"I can,
  I can,
If I try, try, try."

Dragon Dream

I dreamt I rode a dragon,
I rode him up and down,
I rode him to the beach,
I rode him into town,
I rode him on the highway,
I rode him to the zoo,
And all my friends were shouting,
"We want to ride him, too!"

Mr. Wind

Mr. Wind
Blows on the window
He tugs at the tree
He rattles on the door knob,
But he can't get me!

What Is . . . ?

What is over the mountain?
What is under the sea?
What is behind the clouds?
What is inside a tree?

Grandpa

Grandpa is old.
He is older than me,
But he is not as old
As the sky or the sea.

Grandpa is big.
He is bigger than me,
But he is not as big
As the old oak tree.

Grandpa is smart.
He is smarter than me,
But I'll be smart
When I'm 63.

Morning and Night

"It's morning,
It's morning,"
I heard the birds say.
"Get up,
Get up,
And start another day."

It's night time,
It's night time,
The moon is in the sky.
The birds are sleeping
And so must I.

The Moon

Why does the moon
go big and small?
Why doesn't it stay
like a big silver ball?